RHYMES with ORANGE

A CARTOON COLLECTION
BY HILARY B. PRICE

**Andrews McMeel
Publishing**

Kansas City

Rhymes With Orange is syndicated internationally by King Features Syndicate, Inc. For information write King Features Syndicate, Inc., 216 East 45th Street, New York, New York 10017.

Rhymes With Orange copyright © 1997 by Hilary B. Price. All rights reserved. Printed in the United States of America. No part of this book may be used or reproduced in any manner whatsoever without written permission except in the case of reprints in the context of reviews. For information, write Andrews McMeel Publishing, an Andrews McMeel Universal company, 4520 Main Street, Kansas City, Missouri 64111.

www.andrewsmcmeel.com

ISBN: 0-8362-3655-6

Library of Congress Catalog Card Number: 97-71634

──── **ATTENTION: SCHOOLS AND BUSINESSES** ────

Andrews McMeel books are available at quantity discounts with bulk purchase for educational, business, or sales promotional use. For information, please write to: Special Sales Department, Andrews McMeel Publishing, 4520 Main Street, Kansas City, Missouri 64111.

Acknowledgments

There are a ton of people I need to thank, and I bet I am missing more than a few. They are Jay Kennedy, Liz, Rachel, Anne, Laurel, Katie, Jordie, Susan, Kelly, Barce, Rich, Tom, Kajun, Rebecca, Kristin, Dylan, Myra, Kleigh, Ellen, Martha, Lance, Vincent, Dan, Alton, 147 Bartlett, Spa 2608, Rosalie Wright, Bay-TV, the folks at King Features, and Stephanie at AMP. And, especially, my family. Beyond this list, there have been various people's roommates, sweeties, and parents pressed into servitude who have contributed their time and humor to *Rhymes With Orange*. Thank you so much.

Introduction

As a sticky, unkempt child, I liked to rummage through my grandmother's kitchen drawers. My favorite item was her wooden-handled eggbeater. I was also partial to the whisk and the potato masher, but anybody who's spent any time with an eggbeater knows that most everything else pales in comparison.

My grandparents' kitchen was small, and lit from the ceiling by halo-shaped flourescent bulb. To turn it on, my grandfather flicked the switch on the wall, then had to stand up on a kitchen chair to touch the bulb with an outstretched finger. Once he made contact, the bulb sputtered to life. The wiring was screwy, and probably an easy repair. Nevertheless, this practice continued each and every time they turned on the light, for at least twenty-five years.

Now what does this have to do with cartooning? Nothing much, except to illustrate the love I have for pedestrian objects, as well as a genetic predisposition to habitual disorder. These tendencies have influenced both what I write about and the way in which I approach it.

So while some people think in the big picture, or in numbers, or in the ethereal, I tend to focus on the small but concrete. I write and draw about the things all of us do, but either don't think to mention, don't count as important, or hope nobody saw.

I hope you enjoy this collection, culled from the first two years of *Rhymes With Orange*. The strips are placed pretty much in the order that I drew them, so the style changes a little as I figure out what I'm doing.

Oh, I almost forgot. Why the title *Rhymes With Orange*? No other word in the English language rhymes with the word *orange*. I chose the title as a way to show the singularity of the strip's perspective—one that highlights the trials of my own life and those of my friends—trials not traditionally represented on the comics page.

Door hinge is the closest rhyme, but I don't think it quite makes the grade. However, to satisfy those with more coarsely trained ears, I renamed the strip *Rhymes With Door Hinge* for just one day: April Fools' Day, 1996.

—Hilary B. Price, August 7, 1997

HOW SODA CANS WORK

what you may drink.

what must be preserved so it will spill in the back seat of your car.

HILARY B. PRICE

the PARENT-TEACHER CONFERENCE

He's bossy and talkative. Fortunately for him, these will be seen as leadership qualities later on.

"Thanks to J.G." PRICE

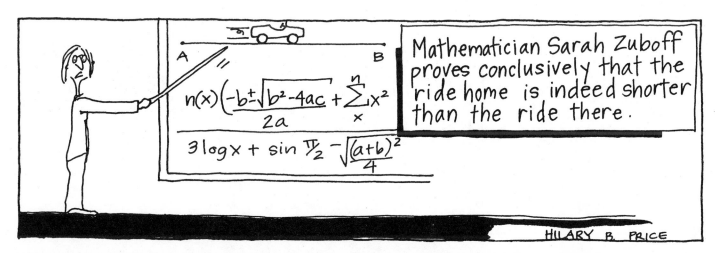

Mathematician Sarah Zuboff proves conclusively that the ride home is indeed shorter than the ride there.

HILARY B. PRICE

7

WHAT'S WRONG HERE?

CALORIES: 0	CALORIES: 0	CALORIES: 0
INGREDIENTS: water, bubbles, precarious artificial sweetener.	INGREDIENTS: water, bubbles.	INGREDIENTS: water.
COST: 79¢	COST: $1.49	COST: $2.99

Diet lem-*lime · SELTZER · FRENCH SPRING WATER

THE BIG QUESTIONS of LIFE, IN REVERSE

Is there life after death?

Will there be grandchildren?

Should I invest in mutual funds?

How many kids?

Should I marry this person?

Where will I go to college?

Will I ever fall in love?

Do I run down the hall with these scissors, or _not_?

HILARY B. PRICE

PROOF of PARALLEL UNIVERSES

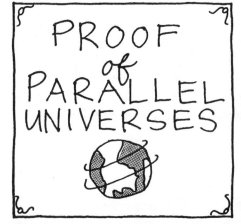

1. you.

2. what your parents think of you.

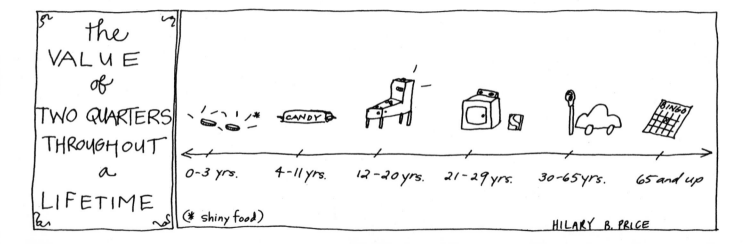

RHYMES with ORANGE

IMPOSSIBLE THINGS TO THROW AWAY

1.
coins from other countries.

2.
"IF YOU WANT MY MONEY, AND YOU THINK I'M SEXY..."
tapes you wouldn't be caught dead listening to now.

3.
keys from places you don't live anymore.

4.
personally significant seashells.

5.
570LRX
the license plate from the car you totalled.

6.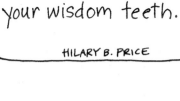
your wisdom teeth.

HILARY B. PRICE

STOP! WAIT! COME BACK!

ACME GARBAGE

BEHIND the SCENES at the AUTO SHOP

NOW HIRING

Hello, my name is Michelangelo Fredericks.

Yes, my name is Eduardo Cisterna Banderas...

Wesley Richards III...

MICK   EDDY   BUTCH

MAGNETIC NORTH POLE

It was a glorious moment, until they realized they had erased all their credit cards.

HILARY B. PRICE

INVISIBLE FURNITURE WAVES (a guide)

open!   nap!   leave!

PRELUDE TO A KISS...

① Make a wildly inconvenient visit.

Elapsed time: 5-20 min.

② Sit in parked car, talking. (No contact.)

So, have any brothers or sisters?

Elapsed time: 1-6 hrs.

③ Are your hands the same size? Check...

Elapsed time: 10 sec. (This is your chance.)

HILARY B. PRICE

Common Knowledge:

Cow lies down in the field → it's going to rain.

Uncommon Knowledge:

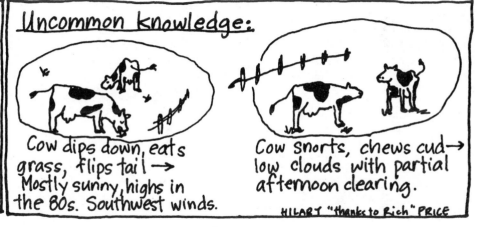

Cow dips down, eats grass, flips tail → Mostly sunny, highs in the 80s. Southwest winds.

Cow snorts, chews cud → low clouds with partial afternoon clearing.

HILARY "thanks to Rich" PRICE

MARKERS of MATURITY

1. Replacing the empty roll of toilet paper with a fresh one, and actually putting it on the thingy.

begone!

no! no! no!

2. Removing empty shampoo bottle, now full of cold, icky water, from ledge of tub.

3. Cleaning out lint from the dryer and throwing it away. (Leaving it on top does not count.)

no!

HILARY B. PRICE

Sylvia checked the social climate, then begrudgingly went to shave her legs.

HILARY B. PRICE

the SINGLE LIFE

You know how they say if you make a space for something, the universe will provide it for you?

sort of.

Think it'll work?

HILARY "Thanks to Lynn" PRICE

THE SMALL CHILD'S THEME PARK

NAPS

WELCOME

EXIT

The Back Seat Game
Put quarter in slot. See how many times you can kick the front seat.

—pop!—
—pop!—
—pop!—

House o' Packing Bubbles

The Rainy Day Game
Run around the dining room table while throwing precious glass figurines.

scuff-your-party-shoes walkway

Hourly Contest!

food mart

Who can throw the best tantrum in the supermarket? Winner gets more precious glass figurines.

HILARY PRICE

PHILOSOPHICAL HIGHLIGHTS

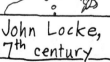

We are a blank slate when we are born. Experience alone makes us.

John Locke, 17th century

We can not know a thing-in-itself as it is, but only as our mind constitutes it.

Emmanuel Kant, 18th century

From each according to his ability to each according to his need.

Karl Marx, 19th century

Can she who eats animal crackers still call herself a vegetarian?

Fernanda Wiggins, 3AM on a Tuesday

HILARY B. PRICE

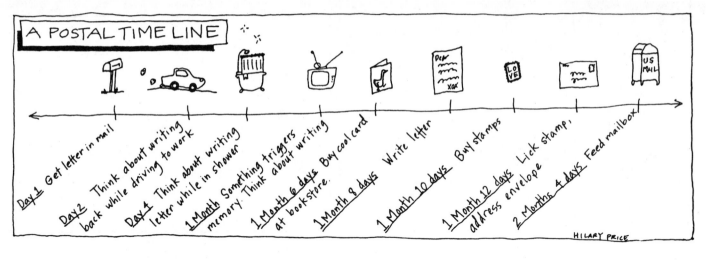

WEIRD VANITY TRUTHS (a saga)

WHAT REALLY HAPPENS IN DRESSING ROOMS

Walk in. Check out what you're wearing.

Check out face.

Take off clothes. Look sideways in mirror.

Look sideways in mirror.

Check out face.

Get dressed. Check out what you're wearing. Leave.

zip! GASP FOR BREATH

unzip! BREATH

Try on clothes. Take them off.

HILARY B. PRICE

NO MORE THAN SIX ITEMS ALLOWED IN THE DRESSING ROOM ~~AT ONCE.~~ AT FIRST.

RHYMES with ORANGE

THINGS THAT SHOULD BE INSURED

ACME insurance

LIP BALM

Replacement for loss or accidental exposure to washing machine.

EARRINGS
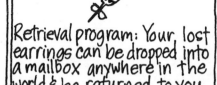
Retrieval program: Your lost earrings can be dropped into a mailbox anywhere in the world & be returned to you.

SUNGLASSES

Policy covers related loss as well as smushed-on-the-car-seat incidents.

LIGHTER

Based on the overwhelming odds that it <u>will</u> disappear, a new one will be sent to you every other week.

REMOTE CONTROL

A qualified service person will switch channels for you until a replacement can be sent.

FANCY PENS

Replacement comes with replica of the original "Happy Graduation" card.

HILARY B. PRICE

INNATELY AGGRESSIVE INANIMATE OBJECTS: a study

DISHWASHER DOOR

PROFILE: Feeds in evenings. Prefers shins.

HILARY B. PRICE

SHOWER CURTAIN

PROFILE: Feeds in early morning. Waits, then envelops leg area. Further grosses out victim with mildew.

CUPBOARD

PROFILE: Most dangerous—attacks randomly. Goes exclusively for head region. (Ring leader.)

Tired of secretarial work, Gladys looked for openings as queen.

HILARY B. PRICE

Hello, who went to Price Club?

SKIN SOFT

HILARY B. PRICE

if DADS WROTE GREETING CARDS

HAPPY BIRTHDAY → DON'T FORGET TO CHANGE YOUR OIL

MERRY X-MAS → HOW'S WORK?

HAPPY EASTER → HERE'S AN ARTICLE FROM THE WALL STREET JOURNAL

HILARY B. PRICE

HOW TO MAKE A HOUSE A HOME

① Throw coffee on rug.

② Blow out porch light.

③ Put dried-up pens beside phone. Hide paper.

HILARY B. PRICE

WHO REALLY COINED the PHRASE?

"Absence makes the heart grow fonder."

—**Frank Tims**, Assistant Postmaster, in support of slothful delivery service.

"Out of sight, out of mind."

—**Becky Banks**, mother of three, upon discovery of furry Rice-A-Roni in fridge.

"No news is good news."

—**Ted Simps**, creative mastermind behind vapid network news programming.

HILARY B. PRICE

CHECKLIST FOR A SUMMER HOUSE ☑

☐ Wooden Wilson tennis racket

☐ pack of 50 cards (Compliments of airline)

☐ miniature golf score sheet

☐ too-small slicker (reversible)

☐ raft with slow leak

☐ mesh/polyester baseball cap — Lloyd's Towing

☐ "Free with fill-up" glasses from gas station — 49ers CELTICS

☐ wiffle bat

☐ paperback copy of Shōgun

☐ cardboard salt and pepper shakers

☐ 8-year-old Yellow pages — 1987-1988

☐ one stray thong

HILARY B. PRICE

NOT feeling like A RESPONSIBLE ADULT? (a few things you can do in a pinch)

Umm, hello?

Make a dentist appointment. (IT DOESN'T MATTER IF YOU SHOW UP OR NOT, YOU JUST NEED TO CALL)

what's that?
neat.
your engine

Get your oil changed.

HILARY B. PRICE

US NEWS WORLD REPORT
THE DOW JONES INDUSTRIAL
BLACK COFFEE, NO SUGAR

Subscribe to U.S. News and World Report.

cool spinning machine

Bring something to the dry cleaner. (YOU MUST PICK IT UP WITHIN A MONTH, OR NO DICE.)

SYNERGISTIC MOMENTS in WORLD HISTORY

Someone pours the first ceramic mold...

HILARY B. PRICE

...Mantelpieces are invented.

Synthetic wood panelling arrives on the scene...

GOSH, WE HAVE THESE BEAN-BAG CHAIRS AND THIS SHAG RUG, WHERE SHOULD WE PUT THEM?

...Our thirst for a rumpus room is born.

Fake plants hit the marketplace...

HOW GRAND! HOW LUSH!

...Hotel lobbies and office parks spring forth across the nation.

BLUE CHIP STOCKS for SUMMER

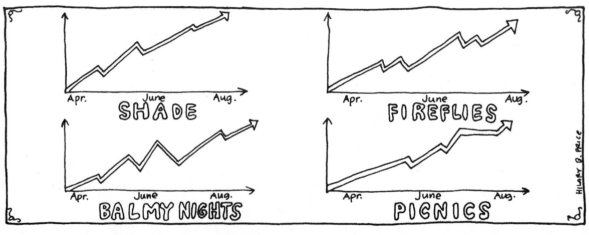

SHADE

FIREFLIES

BALMY NIGHTS

PICNICS

HILARY B. PRICE

MANUEVERING in CORPORATE AMERICA
(a mini-series)

I love cantaloupe.

Pandas rock.

I haven't called Uncle Lou in a while.

scratch

Although Casual Day wasn't officially until Friday, Claude allowed himself a few casual thoughts throughout the week.

HILARY "Thanks to Linda" PRICE

I keep expecting someone to come in and arrest me for impersonating an adult.

HILARY "Thanks to Sarah" PRICE

mutual of OMAHA presents: THE LIFE CYCLE & HABITS of a PENCIL.

HILARY B. PRICE

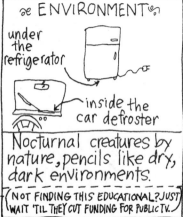

∾ ENVIRONMENT ∾

under the refrigerator

inside the car defroster

Nocturnal creatures by nature, pencils like dry, dark environments.

(NOT FINDING THIS EDUCATIONAL? JUST WAIT 'TIL THEY CUT FUNDING FOR PUBLIC TV.)

∾ COMING of AGE ∾

Each pencil must endure a grueling solo journey from the desk drawer to the space behind the drawer, making it impossible to close.

∾ REPRODUCTION ∾

hubba hubba

Pencils are loners by nature, except when people are moving. This causes a mating frenzy, and the pencil population multiplies.

RHYMES with ORANGE

THE MATH CONSPIRACY

Everything at the convention was going smoothly, until suddenly...

SPROING!

Mrs. Mildred P. Bailor, of Delphine, Wisconsin, stormed in from out of NOWHERE and challenged the ENTIRE mathematical notion of SURFACE AREA...

"WHY is it," she demanded,

"that when you rewrap banana bread in tin foil,

"after eating some,

"the foil will NEVER cover it all the way,

$2x + 4 > y =$ tinfoil

"even though there is LESS to wrap?"

tap! tap! tap!

" any one?"

Nobody stirred. But that night, Mildred Bailor disappeared, never to be seen or heard of again.

THE END

HILARY B. PRICE

$2x^2 + 4xy$

RHYMES with ORANGE

ONE GLASS'S JOURNEY from the BEDROOM back to the KITCHEN	DAY 1	DAY 2	DAY 3	DAY 4	DAY 5
	Bring glass of water to bedside table.	Nothing.	Nothing.	Think about bringing glass back. Forget.	Pick up glass. Phone rings. Put glass down.

DAY 6	DAY 7	DAY 8	DAY 9	DAY 10 VICTORY!	EPILOGUE There is a way to avoid this whole, torrid cycle... On day 1, spill water (it'll dry) and turn glass into a pencil jar.
Arrival of 2nd glass of water to bedside table.	1st glass starts to collect lint.	Throw leftover, linty water on undeserving plant.	Arrival of 3rd glass of water to bedside table.	1st glass makes it to sink, where it will rest, exhausted for several days.	HILARY B. PRICE

WORLD-SHAPING RELIGIOUS DOCTRINES

THE TORAH | THE KORAN | THE NEW TESTAMENT | CONSUMER REPORTS

WHAT AMERICAN CULTURE HAS FAILED TO PREPARE US FOR

To date, we are socially ill-equipped to deal with each other in elevators.

We hear what everyone else is saying in their cubicle, but we pretend like we don't. There is no recourse for this.

THE ROBBERY'S TONIGHT

There is no good answer to the question, "What's up?"

Good! Fine, thank you!

I am so unhip.

BIG FAT EUPHEMISMS (a working guide)

This job involves Data Processing and Customer Relations...

I see. So I'll type and answer the phone.

HILARY B. PRICE

30

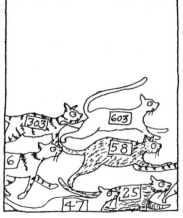

Missionary Martha reaches a weird standpoint in her career when she realizes the tribeswomen have little use for the term "unsightly body hair."

at the NORTH POLE LAUNDR -O- MAT

Putting the "fun" back into "dysfunctional."

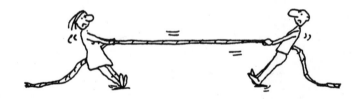

BETWEEN VISITS

GOOD FOR YOU!

HILARY B. PRICE.

So I told Mom, and that was a BIG load off my mind.

GOOD. AND THEN WHAT?

She herself seemed relieved about the whole thing.

GOOD! HOW DID IT MAKE YOU FEEL?

Good. It felt good.

Janice found immense pleasure in her pull-n'-speak therapist.

THE TROUBLED LIFE of WILLIAM SHAKESPEARE, were he around today

Overwhelmed by the fast pace of city life, he records lonely soliloquies on his answering machine.

"You taught me language, and my profit on it is, I know how to curse!... Leave me a message."

HILARY B. PRICE

His funny getup and strange accent get him only bit parts in the theater world.

Here's the head.

Finally, after rejection from every major publishing house, he creates his own 'Zine. Things are better.

MUCH ADO 'FER NUTHIN'

OUT DAMNED SPOT

EXPLAINING HEALTH CARE to CHILDREN

LESSON 1: The "Pre-Existing Condition"

If you already have a cut, I can't give you a band-aid.

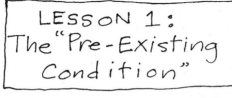

HILARY B. PRICE

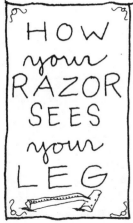

THE MOTHERHOOD MANIFESTO: selected excerpts of CHOICE PROPAGANDA

"DON'T CHEW THAT PENCIL, YOU'LL DIE!!"

This boy once put a too-tight rubber band around his wrist and, TWO seconds later, his hand fell right off!

HELP US!

Last year, 32 youths crossed their eyes-- ALL 32 stuck that way for good.

HILARY B. PRICE

DAY 1

buy now and get a FREE VIDEO!!

DAY 2

One day a girl didn't sit up straight, and she woke up with a hunchback the very next day!

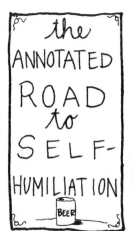

the ANNOTATED ROAD to SELF-HUMILIATION

BEER

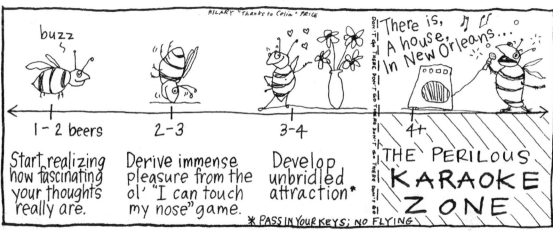

HILARY "Thanks to Celia" PRICE

buzz

1-2 beers — Start realizing how fascinating your thoughts really are.

2-3 — Derive immense pleasure from the ol' "I can touch my nose" game.

3-4 — Develop unbridled attraction*

There is, A house, In New Orleans...

DON'T GO THERE DON'T GO THERE DON'T GO THERE DON'T GO

4+ THE PERILOUS KARAOKE ZONE

* PASS IN YOUR KEYS; NO FLYING

YOUR LIFE as portrayed through Calcium

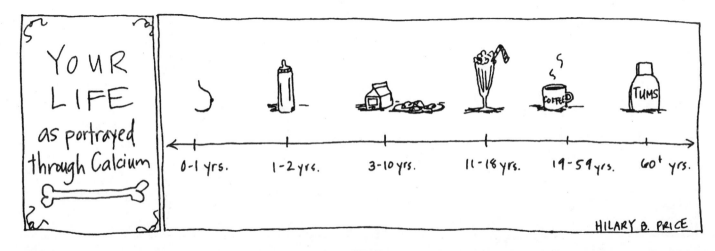

0-1 yrs.   1-2 yrs.   3-10 yrs.   11-18 yrs.   19-59 yrs.   60+ yrs.

HILARY B. PRICE

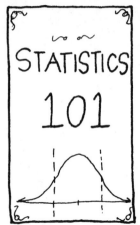

STATISTICS 101

The assignment says go ask 50 people the exact same question...

scritch scritch

But why not ask myself the same question 50 times, and use that?

HILARY B. PRICE

I wonder if I'm the first **GENIUS** to think of this?

LADIES & GENTLEMEN OF THE HOUSE, THE AMERICAN PEOPLE HAVE SPOKEN...

Would you like to go upstairs and play Health Maintenance Organization?

HILARY B. PRICE

LIMITS to LIBERTY

Liberty / Reality

THE AIRPORT:

X-RAY

"In the name of safety, we reserve the right to search all bags."

THE BAR:

JACK'S

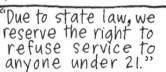

"Due to state law, we reserve the right to refuse service to anyone under 21."

THE CONVENIENCE STORE:

BI-RITE
BEER
CIGARETTES
SODA

"Because it's late and we're open, we reserve the right to a 200% markup on year-old cake mix."

HILARY "Thanks to Liz" PRICE

I'M NOT MARRIED, I DON'T RUN A PRIVATE CONSULTING FIRM CALLED "MYRA & ASSOCIATES," AND I DRIVE A CAR WITHOUT AIR CONDITIONING...

In the interest of maintaining a bell curve, Myra sat down to write her alumni magazine.

HILARY B. PRICE

THE MOST IGNORED PIECES of PAPER of ALL TIME

Magazine Subscription Cards
Useless, except to doctors who trace stolen magazines from their office.

HONEY, FIX THE TRACKING...

The Video Rental Receipt
Wiles away its days on top of the TV until-- 1.) you move 2.) your parents visit.

Appliance Warranty Survey Mailers
Do you like hiking? Gardening? They'll never find out.

The Letter From Your Congressman
Now you see it, Now you don't.

HILARY B. PRICE

COWS at ELLIS ISLAND

No, it's not Holberg. It's Holstein.

HILARY B. PRICE

39

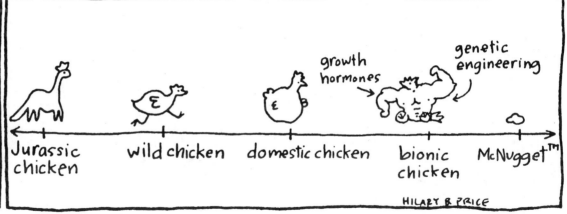

RHYMES with ORANGE

READING HIDDEN WEALTH a guide to assessing your neighbor's paycheck	*Lesson* **1**	Having Kleenex™ prominently displayed in your home is a sign of prosperity. (Poor people use toilet paper.)	
	Lesson **2**	The higher their bed, the richer they are.	
	Lesson **3**	Wealth is statistically dependent on whether or not the dog is allowed on the couch.	

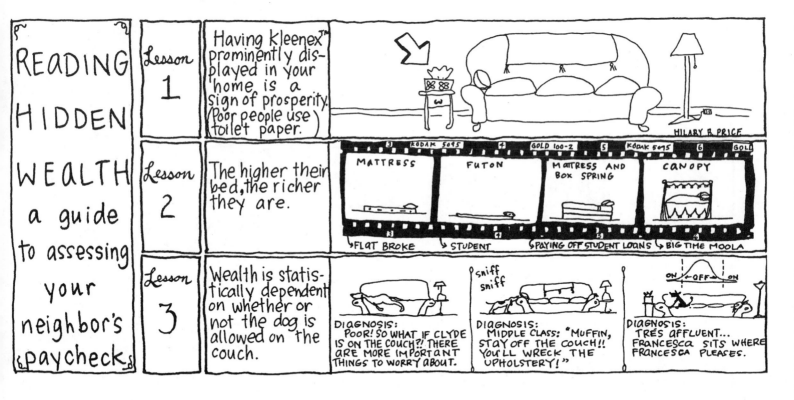

HILARY B. PRICE

MATTRESS — FLAT BROKE
FUTON — STUDENT
MATTRESS AND BOX SPRING — PAYING OFF STUDENT LOANS
CANOPY — BIG TIME MOOLA

DIAGNOSIS: POOR! SO WHAT IF CLYDE IS ON THE COUCH?! THERE ARE MORE IMPORTANT THINGS TO WORRY ABOUT.

sniff sniff
DIAGNOSIS: MIDDLE CLASS: "MUFFIN, STAY OFF THE COUCH!! YOU'LL WRECK THE UPHOLSTERY!"

DIAGNOSIS: TRÉS AFFLUENT... FRANCESCA SITS WHERE FRANCESCA PLEASES.

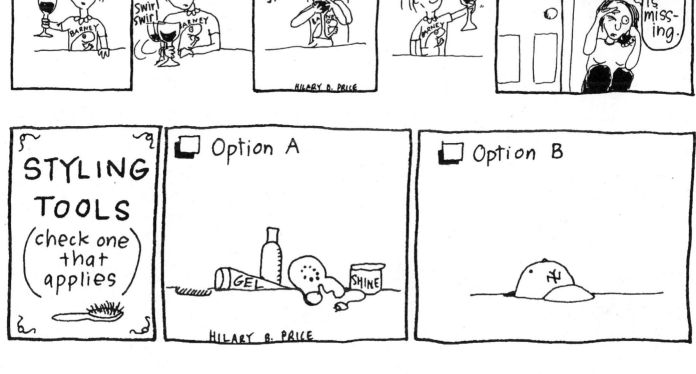

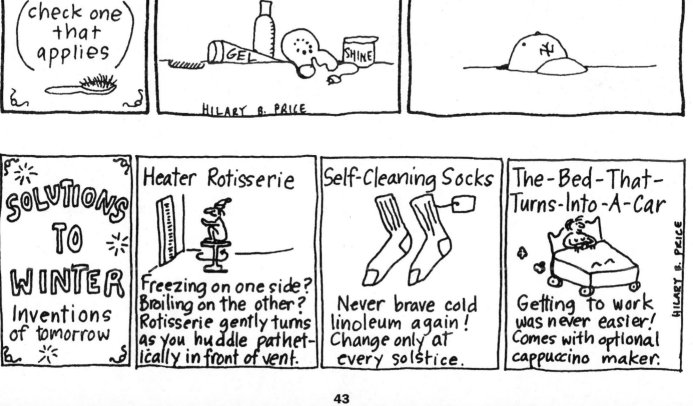

RHYMES with ORANGE

YOUR PARENTS ARE COMING TO VISIT — WHAT IS YOUR PLAN OF ACTION?

① Buy cleaning paraphernalia and clear off surfaces. (Greatly helped by step 2.)

② Hide all pictures and postcards with swear words, nudity or leftist radical propaganda.

I am spineless.

barren refrigerator

③ Turn books of the same nature spine-side in. (Even if you did read them for school.)

THE JOY OF COOKING

THE 7 HABITS OF HIGHLY EFFECTIVE PEOPLE

WHAT COLOR IS YOUR PARACHUTE

④ Stock cupboard with stuff besides ramen noodles. Prominently display fruit.

⑤ Retrieve from deep hibernation all those "It's the thought that counts" Christmas clothes*

what year is it?

where am I?

* Display near fruit.

⑥ Shovel out back seat of car. Practice driving slowly.

STAY ALIVE, 55.
STAY ALIVE, 55.

⑦ Throw the "you-know-whats" into the very back of the nightstand drawer.

⑧ Take a deep breath. Are you ready?

DING DONG

DING DONG

HILARY B. PRICE

your LAUNDRY BASKET (a breakdown)

← Last week's clothes.

← The week before last's clothes.

← Bright colors to be washed separately.*

← Clothes you forgot you had.

← Fine washables.* _____

← What is probably compost by now.

(* THESE CLOTHES ARE ESSENTIALLY ON PERMANENT EXHIBIT IN YOUR BASKET.)

HILARY B. PRICE

BRADY BUNCH EXPOSÉ

6 children, 1 bathroom AND **NOBODY** COMPLAINED OF A FREEZING COLD SHOWER?!

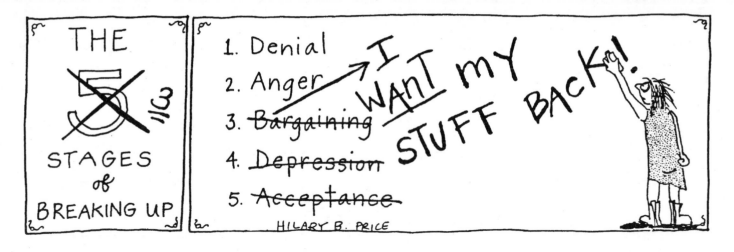

THE ~~5~~ 3 STAGES of BREAKING UP

1. Denial
2. Anger → I WANT MY STUFF BACK!
3. ~~Bargaining~~
4. ~~Depression~~
5. ~~Acceptance~~

HILARY B. PRICE

HOW TO DEAL *with* YOUR CAR *when* IT MAKES WEIRD NOISES

STEP 1: Ignore it. keep driving. Hope it goes away.

CLICK click CLICK click click CLICK CLICK

STEP 2: No improvement? Let it sit in the driveway and work out its own problems.

TALK TO ME

STEP 3: Feeling brave? Open the hood. Prod hopefully.

poke

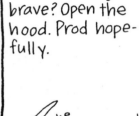

STEP 4: Shell out $500.*

*NOTE THAT WE'VE BEGUN TO TREAT OUR CARS THE SAME WAY WE TREAT OUR HEALTH.

HILARY B. PRICE

---

*at THE PARTY (which one are you?)

I AM SO HANDSOME

I AM SO INTELLECTUAL

I AM SO FUNNY

I FEEL LIKE A BIG BLOCK OF CHEESE.

!!

HILARY B. PRICE

DEFENDING THE DRIVEWAY
(a trans-continental exploration)

THIS IS **MY** F------ DRIVEWAY

New York

TIRE TRACKS'LL LOOK REAL PURDY ON TOP OF YOUR CAR

Dallas

VISUALIZE BEING TOWED.

San Francisco

Anthropologist Lula Huston discovers cave drawings depicting what appears to be static cling.

ROMANTIC APELLATIONS
(a seasonal overview)
SUGAR

Spring

my apple blossom! my honey bee!

Summer

my turtle dove! my sweet pea!

Fall

my trick or treat! my pumpkin pie!

Winter

my cherry Vicks! no, my cherry Vicks

WHAT GOES WRONG?

Everyone enjoying themselves?

HILARY B. PRICE

CHILDHOOD: IMAGINARY FRIENDS

WHAT are you looking at?!

ADULTHOOD: IMAGINARY ENEMIES

HOW AMERICANS DRESS a laundry time line

rattiest denim, best undies

blouses & pleats, 2nd tier undies

fancy shmancy, wedgie city

quality / UNDERWEAR CLOTHING / time

fresh, clean laundry!

1–6 days

7–12 days

13 days and beyond...

(AMERICANS DRESS MOST NICELY WHEN THERE'S NOTHING CLEAN TO WEAR.)

SCANDAL on CAPITOL HILL

ALL THOSE IN FAVOR OF PRESERVING OPEN SPACE AREAS, SAY "AYE."

Aye.

FRESHMAN #1 FRESHMAN #2 FRESHMAN #3 FRESHMAN #4

WHY is Newt staring at us? WHY are the Democrats smiling?

We're voting about golf courses, aren't we? Well, aren't we?

GOP GOP GOP GOP

FRESHMAN #1 FRESHMAN #2 FRESHMAN #3 FRESHMAN #4

HILARY B. PRICE

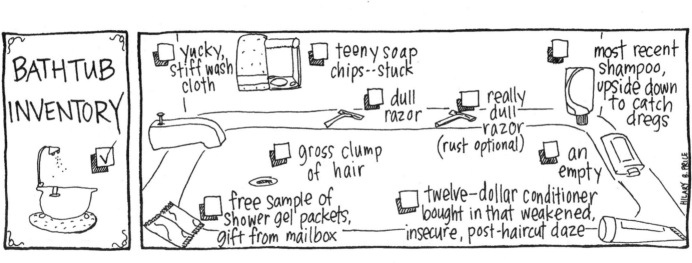

RHYMES with ORANGE

SIGNIFICANT MOMENTS in RABBIT HISTORY

It's Sharon Stone on the line.

Chosen as Easter icon. Makes millions off of plush toys and novelty chocolates.

Whatcha readin'?

The manifesto for Rabbit Nation.

Publication of Watership Down. Immediately canonized alongside Beatrix Potter collection.

Worldwide recognition. President Nixon makes the universal sign for "bunny."

FINISH

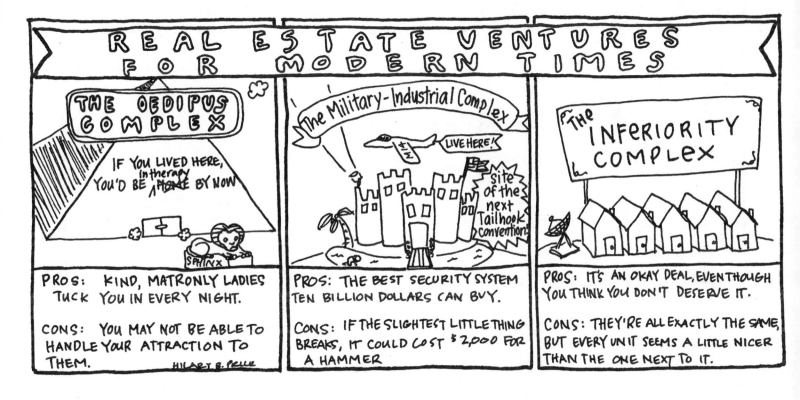

59

THOUGHTS on the V-CHIP... a three-part series

NO PEEKING

Why do you think parents and politicians are spending all this time and money to restrict us from seeing sex on TV?

Obviously, parents are **SO** comfortable talking about sex themselves that they can't BEAR the thought of anyone else teaching it... And politicians, they just don't want to see their personal stories on TV.

HILARY B. PRICE

Part two... THE UNEXPLORED EFFECTS of the "V"-CHIP

Due to sexually explicit material, persons under the age of 18 are restricted from viewing...

Well, we can't watch any on TV, so I guess we could just make out on the couch and see where it takes us.

HILARY B PRICE

PART THREE in the final analysis: THE V-CHIP

This show contains sexually explicit material ... so you can't watch it.

I guess we can't call it the "boob tube" anymore.

HILARY B PRICE

An evening at home with the... BOVINE grammarian

got...?

@!$? It's "HAVE milk", "HAVE milk"!

HILARY B. PRICE

CAT TV

Don't sit so close. You'll wreck your eyes.

HILARY B. PRICE

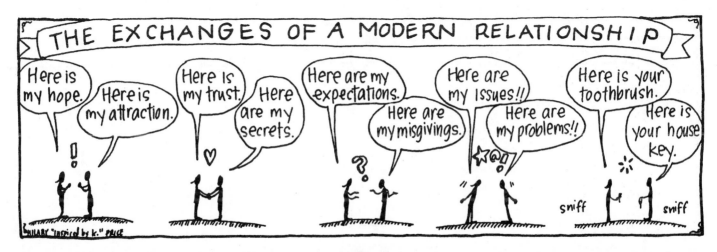

THE EXCHANGES OF A MODERN RELATIONSHIP

Here is my hope.

Here is my attraction.

Here is my trust.

Here are my secrets.

Here are my expectations.

Here are my misgivings.

Here are my Issues!!

Here are my problems!!

Here is your toothbrush.

Here is your house key.

sniff   sniff

HILARY "inspired by k." PRICE

RHYMES with ORANGE

HOW TO RACK UP "INVISIBLE CRUSH" POINTS

Leave a message after the beep...

5 pts.

Indirectly, find out their phone number. Call when you **KNOW** no one's there. Listen to their voice on machine. Hang up. Swoon. Call again. Hang up.

2 pts.

Sit in office. Take blank pad of paper. Write person's name again and again and again. Decorate with hearts and swirls. Throw paper away.

10 pts.

Late at night (or, actually, any time) reroute all errands so you drive by their house. Slow down, but don't stop. Hope they're looking out their window and recognize your silhouette at 50 yards.

*I just **HAD** to stop and say what **nice** shoes you have... Umm, **GREAT** laces, too.*

HILARY B. PRICE

Once you've accumulated 60 crush points, maybe you'll find some lame excuse to introduce yourself...

maybe not.

the MIRACLE WORKERS of MODERN DAY

"Give me something wild and spiky."

HILARY B. PRICE

THE FIRST TWELVE MONTHS

"So what's it like?"

"She cries. She eats. She burps. She poops. She smiles. Her name is Maria, but we lovingly refer to her as 'the attention pit.'"

HILARY B. PRICE

THE FINAL EXAM use EACH WORD IN A sentence THAT demonstrates YOUR UNDERSTANDING OF THE WORD...

1. garish

HE GARISHED THE MEAL WITH A SPRIG OF PARSLEY.

2. curt

MY FAVORITE RELATIVE IS MY UNCLE CURT.

3. iconoclast

"HELLO," SAID I. "HELLO," REPLIED THE ICONOCLAST.

HILARY B. PRICE

RHYMES with ORANGE

If no one you know still drives a Yugo.
Where has it gone on vacation?
And those darn Rubic's Cubes,
  did they get up and move.
Once they failed to provide recreation?

type type

erasable pen

I'll let you in on a secret, they're quite
  safe and sound.
At an island that's sort of a Lost and
  a Found.
It's not on a map, nor a place of distinction.
But we call it home, the Land of
  Extinction.

type type

Here in Jurassic we spurn all that's classic.
Like Plato and Homer and Shakespeare.
We've found the true path can be found
  in New Math.
And lecture King Kong, not King Lear.

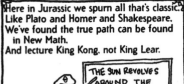

THE SUN REVOLVES AROUND THE EARTH...
Next Week: ESPERANTO

HILARY B. PRICE

In our hierarchy of technology,
The rotary phone still doth ring,
No female or he-male has voice mail
  or e-mail,
And nobody fears Call Waiting.

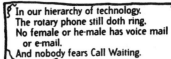

Julie! Gopher! Charo!

THE LOVE BOAT

CRYSTAL PEPSI

In spring we wear terry, in summer
  it's tube tops,
In fall we sport crisp leisure suits,
In winter we're cozy as we trample
  and mosey,
Through snowbanks in neon moon boots.

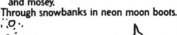

Travolta was here but we lost him
  last year,
The shock left a bit of a sting,
But, turning "retro" is a ticket to go...
There's always the next old thing.

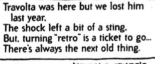

OPENING TONIGHT: KEVIN COSTNER'S WATERWORLD

Last time it was New Coke,
  then eggs without egg yolk,
Remember those disc cameras?
At parties with Dodos we take
  endless photos,
And toast to all that which once was.

BEEN There, Done That

"To things all the rage, trendy, a craze
We say 'No, but *merci beaucoup*.'
Avante garde is too hard, a losing
  trump card—
'Cause you're old for much more
  than you're new."

OBSOLESCENCE NOT ADOLESCENCE

THE LATEST ARRIVAL

WHAT are those?

She's growing hydroponic kitty snacks.

HOW TO TREAT JERKS: a receptionist's guide

IF SOMEONE NEEDS HANGING UP ON, DO IT WHILE YOU'RE IN THE MIDDLE OF TALKING. THEY WILL ASSUME IT IS THEIR OWN FAULT.

Darn phone cut me off again.

MAKE ANGRY REPEAT CALLERS SPELL OUT THEIR NAME AND FIRM EACH TIME. HAVE FUN-- READ THE NUMBER BACK WRONG. SPEAK EXTREMELY SLOW-- THEY ALREADY ASSUME YOU'RE DUMB. MAKE THE MOST OF IT.

Your name's Ed? How many "E's" in Ed?

KEEP IN MIND, THEIR PRESTIGE, WEALTH AND INFLUENCE IS NO MATCH TO YOUR HOLD BUTTON.

chomp chomp

HILARY "Thanks to Kate" PRICE

THE LETTER

Dear Mrs. Barker,   June 6, 1996

I just celebrated my thirtieth birthday, and am taking a moment to reflect on my life and personal growth. I am an almost happy person now, and I wanted you to know the piano lessons you gave me 23 years ago DID NOT HELP.

The theme of my last therapy session was feelings of failure. Of course, your name came up. I am enclosing the bill for that visit.

Fondly yours,   Mary F.

HILARY B. PRICE

Strip 1

HOW TO SELL WATER EFFECTIVELY

(icon for water)

THE BASICS

THERE ARE **TWO** TYPES of WATER: ATHLETIC WATER AND GOURMET WATER

All this time I thought it was salt or fresh!

A.) SPORT FUEL

B.)

TO SELL "ATHLETIC" WATER, GIVE BOTTLE A DISHWASHING-LIQUID SPOUT. PRINT "SPORT" ON THE LABEL. TO SELL "GOURMET" WATER, A COBALT BLUE CONTAINER IS THE WAY TO GO. JACK UP THE PRICE TO MAKE IT SEEM EXTRA SPECIAL.

PREPARING THE MARKET

IT HELPS IF YOU CAN MOLD PUBLIC OPINION TO THINK ALL TAP WATER IS ICKY, POISONIOUS STUFF.

EVIAN

HILARY B. PRICE

FINAL HINTS

This is my water cellar.

ATHLETIC WATER NEEDS AN EXPIRATION DATE. GOURMET WATER SHOULD BE AGED LIKE A GOOD RED WINE.

Strip 2

THE DILEMMA

"Thanks to Liz"

YOU HAVE TWO BASKETS OF IRONING: A BIG BASKET AND A LITTLE BASKET.

Do you...

HILARY B. PRICE

DO THE LITTLE BASKET FIRST SO YOU FEEL LIKE YOU'VE ACCOMPLISHED SOMETHING?

hmm

DO THE BIG BASKET FIRST SO WHEN YOU FINISH IT YOU'VE ONLY A TINY BIT LEFT?

gosh

COMBINE THE TWO, BECOME INTIMIDATED BY THE TASK BEFORE YOU, AND LEAVE.

The choice is suddenly clear.

Strip 3

NO TIME for ENLIGHTENMENT?

(TIPS FOR THE FAST-PACED WORLD)

I CAN'T BELIEVE IT'S NOT BUDDHA!

IS MEDITATION TOO TIME-CONSUMING? NOT GETTING RESULTS FAST ENOUGH? SUPPLEMENT YOUR SPIRITUAL JOURNEY WITH "I CAN'T BELIEVE IT'S NOT BUDDHA!" SLATHER IT ON!

SPEAKING IN TONGUES

WHY SPEND ALL THAT TIME ON A SUNDAY WITH YOUR COMMUNITY? TALK TO YOUR MAKER ON YOUR OWN TIME WITH BERLITZ™ "SPEAKING IN TONGUES." GUARANTEED FLUENCY!

KONFESSION KING!

MENU
- FORGIVENESS
- SALVATK

HILARY B. PRICE

STILL MISBEHAVING, BUT NOT GETTING TO CONFESSION AS MUCH AS YOU SHOULD? TRY THE DRIVE-THRU AT "KONFESSION KING!" YOU'LL FEEL COMPLETELY AT PEACE IN JUST MINUTES.

HOW POLITICS WORK

9:30 AM: A CAT GETS STUCK IN A TREE

meow.

10 AM: REPUBLICAN PRESS CONFERENCE

WHO IS THE MOTHER OF THIS KITTY? WHERE IS SHE? WHAT'S HAPPENED TO THE MORAL FIBER OF OUR COMMUNITY?

GOP in '96!

1 PM: WHITE HOUSE STATEMENT

WHERE IS THE SAFETY NET FOR THIS KITTY? THE GOP HAS PIT BULLS WRITING KITTY PROTECTION LEGISLATION!!

2-5 PM: AIDES ON BOTH SIDES DIG FOR DIRT

YOU SAY THIS CAT HABITUALLY HARASSED YOU?

YOU'RE ADDICTED TO CHEESE, RIGHT?

HILARY B. PRICE.

SIX O'CLOCK NEWS COVER STORY

NEWS

7PM: BI-PARTISAN SUMMIT

LET'S WORK TOGETHER FOR CHANGE!

9 PM:

meow

THE ROUNDS

"Her nose is cold and wet... she's fine."

THE FIRST FEW YEARS OF MEDICAL SCHOOL WERE CHALLENGING FOR REX

HILARY B. PRICE

THE JANITOR'S LAMENT

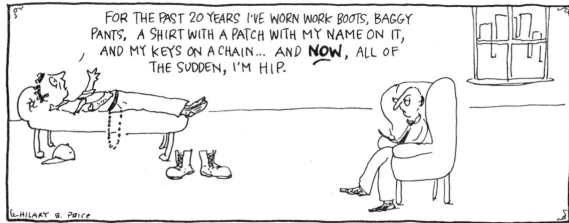

FOR THE PAST 20 YEARS I'VE WORN WORK BOOTS, BAGGY PANTS, A SHIRT WITH A PATCH WITH MY NAME ON IT, AND MY KEYS ON A CHAIN... AND **NOW**, ALL OF THE SUDDEN, I'M HIP.

HILARY B. PRICE

BEDTIME NEGOTIATIONS

munch munch munch

"Yes, cookies have baking soda. No, that doesn't mean you don't have to brush your teeth."

HILARY B. PRICE

THE awakening

Today's Teas
- GARDEN BERRY
- CHAMOMILE-BLOSSOM PEACH
- CITRUS SPICE

PEARL RE-READ THE SELECTION AND STOPPED--AT WHAT POINT HAD TEA BEGUN SOUNDING LIKE ROOM SPRAY?

HILARY B. PRICE

HOW to GET DRESSED UP: his 'n' hers

- match
- iron
- squeeze
- primp
- blow-dry

HILARY B. PRICE

- tuck in shirt

SHOWERS & ROMANCE: the progression

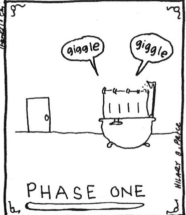

PHASE ONE

PHASE TWO

don't use up the hot water.

PHASE THREE

THE SEVEN DWARFS: where are they NOW?

"HAPPY"™

GOT OVER IT. NOW GOES BY "JADED."

"Grumpy"™

DRINKS A LOT OF COFFEE, HANGS OUT WITH JADED.

"SNEEZY"™

before   after

FIXED THAT DEVIATED SEPTUM, GOT A NOSE JOB.

"DOPEY"™

QUIET OAKS

HILARY B. PRICE

IN AND OUT OF REHAB.

"BASHFUL"™

visualize that cold call...

TRANSFORMATION—DOES MOTIVATIONAL SPEAKING AT HOTELS.

"SLEEPY"™

sniff   I'm not a narcolept, but I play one on TV...

SPOKESPERSON FOR NO-DŌZ.

"DOG"™

THE HEALTH CARE PRACTIONER DOCTOR IS IN

WAS IN PRIVATE PRACTICE, RECENTLY JOINED AN HMO.

whistle while you work..

THE ELECTRIC EELS: an evening at home

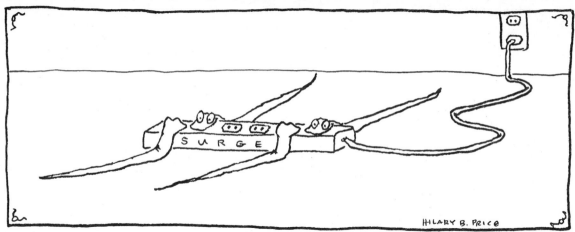

HILARY B. PRICE

it's the RHYMES WITH ORANGE activity hOuR!!

yay!

EVER WANTED TO BE A STAR?
(don't lie, ofcourse you do!)
BUT NOT SURE HOW TO GET THERE?? OUR PANEL OF EXPERTS
(some guys a friend overheard at a café) WILL SHOW YOU HOW TO TAKE
THAT ALL-IMPORTANT **FIRST STEP** ⇒ | CHOOSING A STAGE NAME. |

① Think of your childhood
   pet's name...
② Add your mother's maiden
   name onto that...
   VOILÀ! You're...

SMOKEY GEETTER!

MISTY MERANSKI!

BULLET TURELLE!

(COOL, HUH?)

WHY CHILDREN HAVE a SHORT ATTENTION SPAN

tic tic tic

Possibility A...

HILARY B. PRICE

Possibility B...

click
click
click
·click

RHYMES with ORANGE

TELLTALE SIGNS THAT THE WORLD IS ABOUT TO END... BOOM!!

Federal Espresso? Jammin' Java? Java Joint? Coffee Shop #11?

All taken except that last one.

COPYRIGHT OFFICE

ALL OF THE SUDDEN CAFÉS AND BEAUTY PARLORS RUN OUT OF PITHY NAMES TO CALL THEMSELVES.

WE NEED TWENTIES AND PENNIES!!

THE NEWSSTAND NEXT TO THE SUBWAY MAKES CHANGE FOR ANYONE WHO ASKS--NO PURCHASE NECESSARY.

So I saw the 50-gallon tub of cold cream and asked myself, "Why buy 50 gallons when 5 ounces will do?!"

BUYING IN BULK SLOWLY PETERS OUT AS THE NATIONAL PASTIME.

Do you have Sanka?

Of course.

STAR BUCKS

INSTANT COFFEE MAKES A HUGE COMEBACK.

BY: HILARY "YOU HEARD IT HERE FIRST" PRICE...

This soap won't make you look younger, it's not about being sexy-- it's just, y'know, soap.

ADVERTISERS TELL IT LIKE IT IS.

Sniff sniff

What is it, boy? what is it?!

STAGE SETUP

ACME RENTAL

FOLK SINGER

for voice

for guitar

BARBERSHOP QUARTET

for bass   for baritone   for tenor   for lead

POLITICIAN

for one side of the mouth

for the other side

LIFESTYLES of the UP & COMING...

HOW TO MAKE a HOUSE a HOME

BILL AND I DECORATED THE LIVING ROOM FROM THE "POTTERY BARN" CATALOG... A FEW OVERSTUFFED CHAIRS, A LITTLE WICKER...

THE KITCHEN CAME STRAIGHT OFF THE PAGES OF MARTHA STEWART'S "LIVING"... WE WENT FOR THE HOMEY, RUSTIC LOOK.

WHAT ARE YOU SPRAYING?!

BACON & EGGS ROOM FRESHENER. NEITHER OF US COOKS.

THE SCRUB DOWN

SOAP on ROPE

Y'KNOW, NOT ENOUGH GUYS THESE DAYS TAKE BATHS -- DON'T THINK IT'S MANLY ENOUGH.

HECK, THE **ROMANS** TOOK BATHS -- AND THEY WERE TOTAL STUDS!! YOU JUST GOTTA KNOW HOW TO DO IT RI—

HONEY, HAVE YOU SEEN THE TOILET BRUSH?

WATER VOLUME: a study

7,689,000,000,000,000 gal.
overall effect:
INSPIRATION

NIAGARA

492,000,000 gal.
overall effect:
ROMANCE

383 gal.
overall effect:
HARMONY

drip
drip
drip

.000012 gal.
overall effect:
PSYCHOSIS

ARE YOU **SURE** YOU'RE NOT GETTING ENOUGH EXERCISE?

CONSIDER THIS: WHEN YOU REST, YOU BURN 120 CAL./HR. WHEN YOU JOG, YOU BURN 840 CAL./HR. SO EVERY 7 HOURS OF REST EQUALS ONE JOG... IT'S THAT EASY TO GET INTO SHAPE!

I...feel...the...burn.

ADJUSTING to a NEW HOME: how inanimate objects cope

DISHWARE: FEELS SLIGHTED ABOUT THE MOVE, YET UNABLE TO EMOTE. TURNS ANGER UPON ITSELF.

go away.

KEYS: BECOME UTTERLY AGORAPHOBIC. SEEK OUT SMALL, DARK PLACES TO HIDE AND REST.

SUITCASE: FEELS NEED TO ESTABLISH TERRITORY. DECIDES TO GIVE BIRTH ALL OVER THE ROOM.

THE CONUNDRUM

So, whaddya think? Great huh?

RJR

WELL, THE TOBACCO COMPANIES ARE IN A FINE KETTLE OF FISH.

TOO TRUE.

LEFTY BRIDGE

HILARY B. PRICE

THOSE LEAKS ABOUT THEM KNOWING IT WAS ADDICTIVE FROM THE START... AND HOW THEY WERE SECRETLY AFTER US TEENY-BOPPERS... HOW ARE THEY GOING TO PORTRAY THEMSELVES AS CONCERNED CITIZENS AND STILL MOVE PRODUCT?

IT'LL BE INTERESTING TO SEE HOW THEY'LL MANEUVER IT.

SMOKE LESS. INHALE MORE.

BLACK HOLE EXISTENCE CONFIRMED!

The hall closet of 11A Pine St.

NO ENTRY per U.S. order. Gov't

HILARY B. PRICE

The file cabinet, Bldg 6 NE, Meadowland Industrial Park

CAUTION CAUTION CAUTION CAUTION CAUTION CAUTION

Dryer #17, Bill's Whirl-O-Mat

17. 0. ∅ $18.9. ∅

U.S. MARSHALL

IF CATS WROTE GREETING CARDS

I MISSED YOU

SO I PEED ON YOUR BED.

HAPPY HOUSE-WARMING!

HERE ARE TWO MICE AND A GOPHER.

IN SYMPATHY

I WILL KNEAD YOUR CHEST WHILE YOU SLEEP.

HILARY B. PRICE

It's our Back-to-School Cartoon...

DEMOGRAPHICS of a MILK CRATE

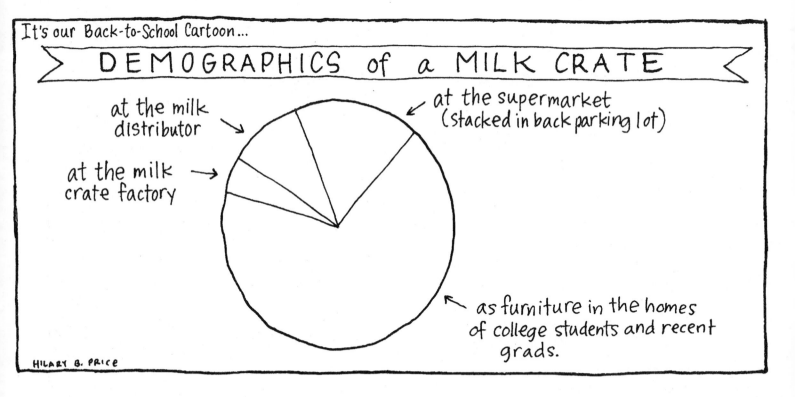

at the milk distributor

at the milk crate factory

at the supermarket (stacked in back parking lot)

as furniture in the homes of college students and recent grads.

HILARY B. PRICE

got milk?

CRATE?

THE LAWS of the LAND: Commandments 11-20

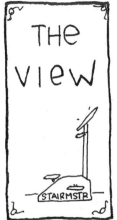

11. THOU SHALT REPACK COMPUTERS IN THEIR ORIGINAL BOXES.

12. THOU SHALT NOT PUT ALUMINUM FOIL IN THE MICROWAVE.

13. RIGHTY-TIGHTY, LEFTY LOOSEY-- I HAVE COMMANDED IT.

14. THOU SHALT HANDLE CDs BY THE EDGES ALONE.

15. THOU SHALT NOT TOP OFF.

16. THOU SHALT WAIT 30 MINUTES AFTER EATING TO SWIM.

17. THOU SHALT STEER INTO A SKID.

18. I COMMAND YE TO WALK LEFT, STAND RIGHT.

19. THOU SHALT CHECK THE EGGS BEFORE BUYING THEM.

20. THOU SHALT **NOT** BRING MORE THAN ONE CARRY-ON ITEM PER PASSENGER.

HILARY "Thanks to Rey" PRICE

The View

STAIRMSTR

I DON'T GET IT. THAT DUDE IS **ALWAYS** AT THE GYM.

HILARY B. PRICE

AFTERNOON REMINISCENCE

YEP, EVERY MAN WANTS COMFORT-- TO GO BACK TO THE DAY WHEN HE WAS JUST A BABE IN HIS MOTHER'S ARMS, SUCKLING INNOCENTLY AT HER BREAST.

THAT BEING THE CASE, I FIND IT TRULY, TRULY AMAZING IT TOOK **SO** LONG FOR THOSE DISHWASHING DETERGENT CAPS TO FIND THEIR WAY ONTO SPORTS DRINKS.

HILARY B. PRICE

THE PEN
part IV

BESIDE THE OBVIOUS METAPHORICAL SIGNIFICANCE, IT'S QUITE ODD THAT THERE'S A YOUNG COW IN THE CUBICLE NEXT TO MINE.

IT'S "CALF."

LISTEN, "CORPORATE COG," I DID SOME RESEARCH, AND IT TURNS OUT THIS OFFICE BUILDING WAS BUILT ON PASTURE LANDS, WITH **NO** REGARD TO ZONING LAWS.

SO?

SO THIS IS MY LAND, PAL.

IN MEMORY OF MY HERD, AND OTHERS WHO HAVE SUFFERED SIMILARLY, I TOOK THE LIBERTY OF EATING THE PLANT NEXT TO THE ELEVATOR.

THE PEN
(the conclusion...)

SO HOW LONG WILL THEY KEEP YOU IN THIS CUBICLE, A.K.A. "THE VEAL FATTENING PEN"?

UNTIL I HIT MY TARGET WEIGHT.

WHICH EXPLAINS THE "SLIM FAST" SHAKES YOU DRINK ALL DAY LONG.

HEY, THIS SETUP'S NOT BAD -- IT'S COMFORTABLE, I GET MY OWN SPACE, THE BENEFITS ARE PRETTY GOOD.

I'M JUST BIDING MY TIME UNTIL I CAN ESCAPE.

I SAID THE SAME THING FIVE YEARS AGO.

THE ART OF STAYING AHEAD

YES, I'M CALLING TO CONFIRM THE CANCELLATION OF THE MEETING WE HAVE YET TO SCHEDULE.

HILARY B PRICE

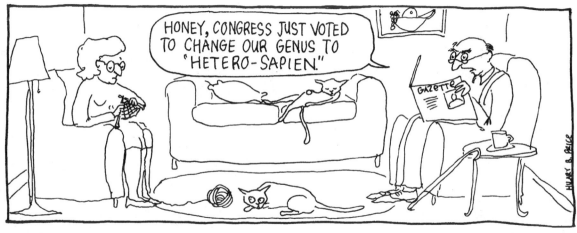

WHEN YOU CAN'T AFFORD A BRASS PLAQUE: alumni giving for English majors

DONATE $25 AND A WHITE MAILING LABEL WITH YOUR NAME ON IT WILL BE AFFIXED, WITH POMP AND CIRCUMSTANCE, TO A MEAL TRAY.

DONATE $40 AND A WHITE MAILING LABEL WILL BE PRINTED **IN PERMANENT INK** AND STAPLED WITH GRATITUDE TO THE UNDERSIDE OF A BENCH.

DONATE $100 AND SPONSOR A **FULL** PASTRY TRAY AT A TRUSTEE MEETING. YOUR NAME WILL PROMINENTLY APPEAR ON A PLACE CARD NEAR THE COFFEE.

IT'S STOPTIONAL

STOP

Thanks to Sarta

REALLY, OFFICER, WHY "PERIOD" WHEN YOU CAN "COMMA"?

Martha perfects the ancient ritual of roll-through justification.

HILARY B. PRICE

DEATH RITUALS from JAPAN

Yesterday

Hara-kiri: (HĀR-I-KĀR-Ē)
Death by disembowelment

Today

Karaoke: (KĀR-Ē-Ō-KĒ)
Death by embarrassment

HILARY B. PRICE

COMMUNE in CRISIS

beep...
beep...

I WANT... A JEEP GRAND CHEROKEE... A GOLDEN RETRIEVER... A PLUCKY WHITE TENNIS SKIRT...

Her fellow members feared the worst... A knock to the head and June had become suburbatose.

HILARY B. PRICE

RHYMES with ORANGE

DIARY OF A SPORT UTILITY VEHICLE IN THE SUBURBS...

Monday: Excitement! Splash in puddle!! (Then go to carwash.)

Tuesday: We hit a pothole!! Thrills galore!!

Wednesday: HEAVY action -- bump garage door.

Thursday: Owner finds scratch... I get detailed.

Friday: Dog rides along! (Followed by ½ hr session with Dust Buster.™)

Saturday: Real gravel road for ¼ mile! We go into 4 WHEEL drive!!!

Sunday: Quiet time in cul-de-sac. Get college alma mater sticker on rear window.

scritch scritch

PAINT

HARVARD

DIARY OF A SPORT UTILITY VEHICLE
DIARY OF A VERY EXPENSIVE MOUNTAIN BIKE
NORDIC TRAC -- MY LONELY LIFE
REFLECTIONS FROM THE BASEMENT --
THE LIFE & TIMES OF A BREAD MACHINE

PILGRIMAGE to the DRUGSTORE

WALVELOPES Letter Size

I GOT THAT STUFF YOU ASKED FOR: ASPIRIN, COLD MEDICINE AND ANTACID.

THANKS.

WAL-BUPROFEN, WAL-FED AND WAL-AIDS?!

OH, AND I BOUGHT SOME FACE LOTION FOR MYSELF.

LET ME GUESS... WAL-OF OLAY?

REFLECTIONS of a SOCCER MOM

TAXI

DURING MY MARRIAGE, MY TWO NAMES WERE "ONE OF US" & "WE WILL."

PARDON?

DAVID ALWAYS SAID TO THE KIDS, "DON'T WORRY, **ONE OF US** WILL GO TO THE GAME." OR, "IT'S OKAY, **WE'LL** PICK YOU UP."

AFTER-DINNER READING

OPENING UP TO YOUR PARTNER

DEFENDING YOURSELF AGAINST VERBAL ATTACKS

HALLOWEEN CANDY: THE CASTE SYSTEM

The Brahmins

Reese's   Kit Kat   M&Ms   SNICKERS   Milky Way   Baby Ruth

2nd Tier

STARBURST   Twizzlers   Skittles   Gum   ← Pixie Sticks   Good 'n' Fruity

3rd Tier

ANYTHING COCONUT

The Untouchables

Raisins   orange sugar circus peanuts ←

HILARY B. PRICE

RULES:

① TRADING CANDY MAY ONLY OCCUR WITHIN CASTES.

② SWIPING TOP TIER CANDY IS A **VERY SERIOUS** OFFENSE.

③ TIER 3 CANDY CAN BE DISTRIBUTED FREELY TO PARENTS.

④ THE UNTOUCHABLES CAN BE USED AS AMMO, OR FED TO PETS, WITHOUT GUILT.

WARNING: Older siblings can & will pillage, regardless of rules.

HALLOWEEN:
the
hidden
agenda

Between each doorbell ring, Rose recalculated the odds of having chocolate leftover.

HILARY B. PRICE

WARHOL?

COSTCO.

HILARY B. PRICE

THE
DRIVE-
THRU
ATM

The Expectation

WE WILL REVOLUTIONIZE THE ACCESSIBILITY OF BANKING FOREVER!!

CLAP CLAP CLAP CLAP CLAP CLAP CLAP

The Reality

HILARY B. PRICE

home for the HOLIDAYS?

HOW TO LET YOUR PARENTS KNOW YOU LOVE THEM

1. Borrow the car. Reset all the radio stations.

2. Leave a trail of wet towels leading from the bathroom.

3. Sleep. A <u>lot</u>.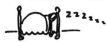

4. Spend the meal hours visiting friends.

5. Let the porch door slam as you enter, <u>especially</u> late, late at night...

☆ Remember: If it fits into your suitcase, it's yours to keep!

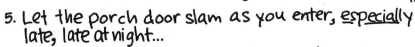

TONIGHT on CROSSFIRE:

LACTOSE INTOLERANCE

I HAVE TO MY RIGHT, DR. LAUREL WIGGINS, PROFESSOR OF GASTROENTEROLOGY AT HARVARD, AND TO MY LEFT, ACTIVIST AND BROWN JERSEY, BESSIE.

THE DYING BREED

see:
www.grammarian.
englishlit.tweed
coat.com

THERE'S **NO** RESPECT FOR THE ENGLISH LANGUAGE ANYMORE!! IT'S BEEN TRUNCATED, MAIMED, REDUCED TO A SERIES OF LAME ABBREVIATIONS!!

I SAY **NO** MORE!! THAT'S IT!! <u>PERIOD</u>!!

YOU MEAN "DOT"?

the
visitor
a week-long series

LOOK AT THEM DOWN THERE! ... LAUGHING, PLAYING, JOYFUL.

OH, TO BE YOUNG AGAIN.

BZZT BZZT

HELLO?

DOWN HERE.

HI. YOU CALLED. I'M FROM THE DEPARTMENT OF YOUR INTERIOR.

WHAT'S THIS?! A HOUSECALL FROM MY INNER CHILD?

LISTEN, I WAS BUSY PLAYING DOCTOR WITH BILLY FROM DOWN THE STREET WHEN I GOT THE PAGE. ARE YOU GONNA LET ME IN?

---

the
visitor
part two

SO IT SAYS HERE ON MY FISHER-PRICE "MY FIRST LAPTOP" THAT YOU WANT TO BE A KID AGAIN.

HAVEN'T WE ALL THOUGHT ABOUT IT?

WELL, AS YOUR INNER CHILD, I'M HERE TO TRAIN YOU.

TRAIN?

WHAT, YOU THINK IT'S EASY?

HERE'S SOME PRELIMINARY READING.

"NEGOTIATING THE FRONT SEAT: CODES 311-499."
"GUM: A POST-MODERN APPROACH."
"WHO FARTED?: THE LIBRETTO."

STUDY UP, AND I'LL BE BACK AT 6AM TOMORROW.

SIX??!

CARTOONS START THEN.

---

the
visitor
part three

In which our heroine's inner child guides her along the path toward youth.

WARNING: PLASTIC BAGS ARE NOT A TOY

PARDON THE IMPOSITION, BUT **WHERE** DO YOU THINK YOU'RE GOING WITH MY FRESH DRY CLEANING?

WARNING: PLASTIC BAGS ARE NOT A TOY

CODE 617: IN PREPARATION FOR CHILDHOOD REVISITATION, THE HOUSE MUST BE CHILDPROOF. BY THE WAY, I NAILED SHUT THE CABINET WITH THE DRANO IN IT.

HILARY B. PRICE

the visitor
part four

In which our heroine's inner child guides her along the path toward youth.

BY THE WAY, YOU'RE GOING TO HAVE TO KICK THE COFFEE HABIT.

I taut I taw a puddy tat...

IT'S SUGAR, BABE, FROM HERE ON OUT. SUGAR CEREAL, CUPCAKES, CANDY BARS. CHILDHOOD IS SPONSORED BY THE SUGAR LOBBY.

KAP'N KRISPIES

HOW DO YOU SURVIVE WITHOUT **REAL** FOOD, **REAL** NUTRITION?

WHAT, LIKE COFFEE?

WE HAVE ANCILLARY DEALS WITH THE HOT DOG INDUSTRY, THE PEANUT BUTTER LOBBY AND THE SPAGHETTI Os COALITION. YOU WANT COFFEE & CIGARETTES? TALK TO YOUR INNER ADOLESCENT.

the visitor
the final episode

In which our heroine returns to reality after a brief jaunt with her inner child.

WHO PUT ALL THOSE STICKERS ON MY ARMOIRE?!

YOU DID.

What's up, Doc?

CRISP-OS

OH, LEO, I'M SO SORRY.

CRISP-OS

KLINK KLANK

Y'KNOW, I DON'T THINK I CAN **DO** THIS SECOND CHILDHOOD THING. I'M **TOO** STUCK IN MY ADULT WAYS! I **CAN'T** LEAVE THEM BEHIND.

CRISP-OS

DON'T FEEL BAD. VERY FEW MAKE IT. MOST OF MY PLAYGROUP ARE MEN IN THEIR FIFTIES.

CRISP-OS

the BIG TALK

sneeze rags

EVERYTHING'S A JOKE TO YOU. YOU'RE NOT SERIOUS. YOU DON'T SHOW ANY COMPASSION.

THAT TICKLES.

Row 1:

want to live alone?

A Rhymes With Orange Field Guide to Renting in a trendy metropolitan area

Part 1 of 3...

FIRST OF ALL, KNOW WHAT MEANS WHAT...

$600? For this?

SMALL STUDIO:

A CRAWL SPACE.

HILARY B. PRICE

SMALL 1 BEDROOM:
A STUDIO WITH A WALK-IN CLOSET LARGE ENOUGH FOR A MATTRESS.

sigh

LARGE 1 BEDROOM:
WILL YOU PLOP DOWN ½ YOUR MONTHLY INCOME ON SHELTER?

2 BEDROOM: Forget it.

OTHER IMPORTANT WORDS:

modern: ugly with low ceilings.

charming:
1. old & decrepit.
2. small & old.

Row 2:

want to live alone?

A Rhymes With Orange Field Guide to Renting in a trendy metropolitan area

Part 2 of 3...

KNOW YOUR AMENITIES!

how festive

PATIO:
A CEMENT SLAB YOU CAN'T PARK YOUR CAR ON.

HILARY B. PRICE

DECK:
1) THE FIRE ESCAPE.
2) A WINDOW BOX.

GARDEN:
1.) A PATCH O' WEEDS
2.) A PILE O' DIRT.

~Advice Section~

Dear RWO,
What does "garage negot." mean?
Clueless

Dear Clueless,
"Garage Negotiable" means "not included" and "expensive." Why not cut costs and just live out of your car instead?

Row 3:

want to live alone?

A Rhymes With Orange Field Guide to Renting in a trendy metropolitan area

Part 3 of 3...

GET TO KNOW YOUR LANDLORD...

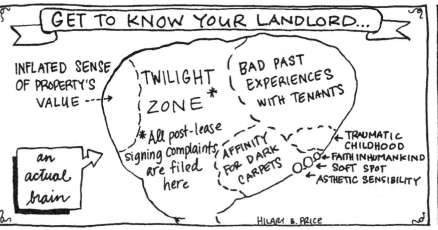

INFLATED SENSE OF PROPERTY'S VALUE

TWILIGHT ZONE *

BAD PAST EXPERIENCES WITH TENANTS

* All post-lease signing complaints are filed here

AFFINITY FOR DARK CARPETS

← TRAUMATIC CHILDHOOD
← FAITH IN HUMANKIND
← SOFT SPOT
← ASTHETIC SENSIBILITY

an actual brain

HILARY B. PRICE

The mind in motion...*
This place has beautiful hardwood floors, a great selling point-- Wait, but what if they get scuffed? What if I decide to move from my posh house to this little studio and the floors are wrecked? No, I better cover the whole thing with industrial carpet.
* A TRUE OCCURENCE!

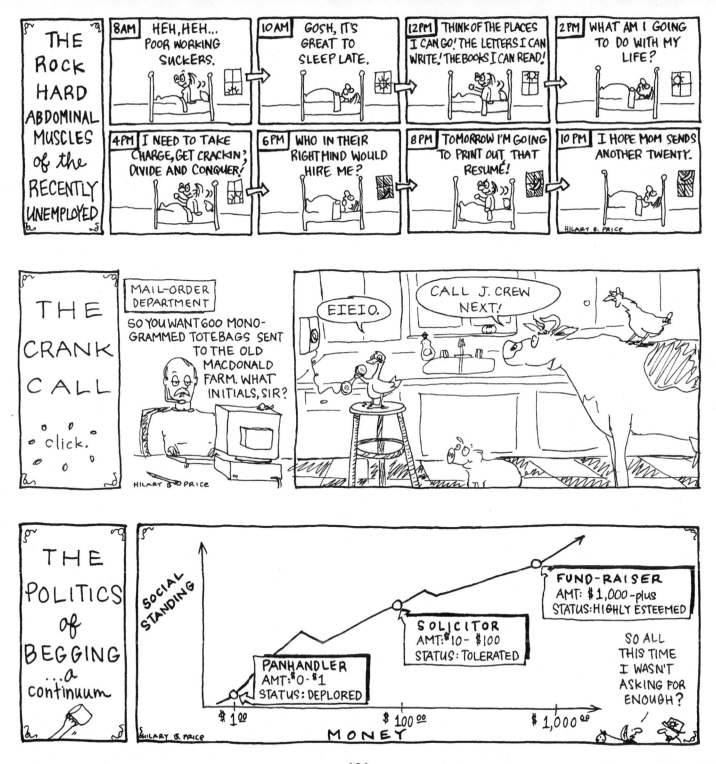

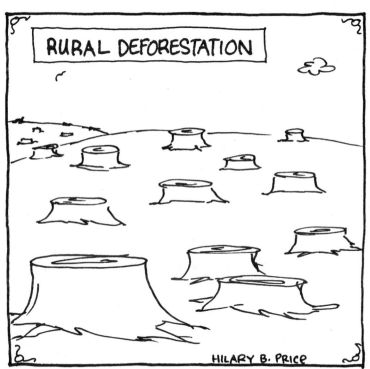

WHAT HAPPENS THE REST of the YEAR

THE FEMININE ~~BLUES~~ pinks

Get her, Duchess! Get her!

I'M FEELING CONFINED BY GENDER STEREOTYPES.

WHAT DO YOU MEAN?

WHAT DID YOU GET FOR CHRISTMAS THIS YEAR?

X-MEN, SOME POWER RANGERS.

SO WHAT HAVE YOU BEEN PLAYING?

WAR OF THE SUPERHEROES. HOW 'BOUT YOU?

ATTACK OF THE "MY LITTLE PONIES."

LOSES ITS KICK, DOESN'T IT?

THE BACK PORCH

THEY'RE SO DRY AND PRIM.

IT'S LIKE SMOOCHING A WAFER.

QUITE VICTORIAN, I'D SAY.

DOGS DISCUSS THE MERITS OF PEOPLE KISSES

TALES from a FIRST JOB

CHAPTER 1: THE INITIATION

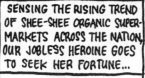

SENSING THE RISING TREND OF SHEE-SHEE ORGANIC SUPERMARKETS ACROSS THE NATION, OUR JOBLESS HEROINE GOES TO SEEK HER FORTUNE...

WHOLLY HOLY ORGANICS — OPENING SOON!

DO YOU SWEAR TO SELL THE FOOD, THE WHOLE FOOD, AND NOTHING BUT THE FOOD, SO HELP YOU GODDESS?

I DO.

MOOSEWOOD

HERE ARE YOUR MANUALS. GROUP TAI CHI BEGINS PROMPTLY AT EIGHT.

TUBERS
LEGUMES
SPROUTS
GREEN LEAFIES
GRAINS

MOM, DAD, I GOT THE JOB! MY TITLE? IT'S, UMM, "PRODUCE HOSTESS."

TALES from a FIRST JOB

CHAPTER 2: IN WHICH OUR HEROINE MEETS THE OTHER HELP AT WHOLLY HOLY ORGANIC FOODS

SO, WHAT'S YOUR JOB?

I'M A PRODUCE HOSTESS.

SOME PEOPLE LEAD MOVEMENTS, SOME LEAD FORTUNE 500 COMPANIES... I LEAD PEOPLE TO PRODUCE.

WHAT ABOUT YOU?

FROMAGE STEWARD.

THE CHEESE AISLE GUY?

TO THE LESS ENLIGHTENED, YES.

TALES from a FIRST JOB

CHAPTER 3: IN WHICH OUR HEROINE FACES THE GRAND OPENING.

9 AM: HI! WELCOME TO WHOLLY HOLY ORGANICS. I'M YOUR PRODUCE HOSTESS. CAN I HELP YOU?

10 AM: WELCOME TO WHOLLY HOLY ORGANICS. I'M YOUR PRODUCE HOSTESS. NEED HELP?

1 PM: WELCOME TO WHOLLY HOLY. I'M YOUR HOSTESS.

3 PM: HI. WHOLLY HOLY HODUCE PROSTESS. HELP YOU?

OLLY-OLLY-IN-COME-FREE TO YOU TOO, LADY.

Tales from a FIRST JOB

CHAPTER 4: IN WHICH OUR HEROINE LEARNS THAT PRESENTATION IS EVERYTHING AT THE WHOLLY HOLY ORGANICS FOOD MARKET.

WHAT'S THIS?!

AN EXACT REPLICA OF L'ARC DE TRIOMPHE IN PARIS.

MADE ENTIRELY OUT OF RED BELL PEPPERS?!

YESIREE.

AND HOW ARE PEOPLE GOING TO BUY RED BELL PEPPERS WITHOUT WRECKING THE DISPLAY??

WAIT. WHAT'S THAT?

THE FRANK LLOYD WRIGHT HOUSE. EACH BRICK—A WEDGE OF SMOKED GOUDA.

Tales from a FIRST JOB

CHAPTER 5: IN WHICH OUR HEROINE LEARNS THE LAYOUT OF THE WHOLLY HOLY ORGANICS FOOD MARKET.

OKAY. DAIRY IS ON AISLE 1. DAIRY-FREE IS ON AISLE 6.

CHECK.

WHEAT IS ON AISLE 2. WHEAT-FREE IS ON AISLE 5.

GOTCHA.

WAIT-- WHAT ARE ON AISLES 3 & 4?

BUFFER ZONE. WE DON'T WANT ANY FIGHTS.

Tales from a FIRST JOB

CHAPTER 6 IN WHICH OUR HEROINE EDUCATES THE MASSES AT THE WHOLLY HOLY ORGANICS FOOD MARKET.

EXCUSE ME? DO YOU HAVE ANY WONDER™ BREAD?

SSHH— DON'T SAY THAT SO LOUD!

PARDON?

IT'S TOO REFINED. WHITE SUGAR, WHITE FLOUR, PERSERVATIVES EVEN!!

I'M SORRY, MA'AM. WE DON'T EVEN STOCK THE INGREDIENTS, LET ALONE THE BREAD.

POT ROAST, THEN?

POT, MAYBE. ROAST, NEVER.

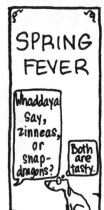

SPRING FEVER

Whaddaya say, zinneas, or snapdragons?

Both are tasty.

I THINK WINTER HAS REALLY GOTTEN TO MOM.

SHE WANTS SPRINGTIME AND SHE WANTS IT BAD.

WHERE IS SHE?

LOCKED IN THE BATHROOM READING THE BURPEE™ SEED CATALOG OUT LOUD TO THE DOG.

AGAIN?

CAUSE AND EFFECT

CYBER AGE...

CYBER AGED.

In the forseeable future...

Spring!

THIS MODEL FEATURES DUAL AIR BAGS, ANTI-LOCK BRAKES, AND THE "MOM-ARM SAFETY DEVICE." BRAKE SUDDENLY, AND THE "MOM-ARM" SHOOTS OUT IN FRONT OF THE PASSENGER. INEFFECTIVE, YET COMFORTING ALL THE SAME.

IDLE MOMENTS

America-on-hold.

America-in-line.

A-O-Hell.

THE PERMUTATIONS WERE IRRESISTIBLE AS SOPHIE AGAIN TRIED TO LOG ON.

HILARY B. PRICE

MONEY-SAVING TIPS for the HEALTH-CONSCIOUS

1. LIVE IN AN AREA WITH GOOD WATER QUALITY... BUY A WATER FILTER ANYWAY.

HILARY B. PRICE

2. NEVER CHANGE THE FILTER.

3. CONGRATULATIONS! YOU ARE THE PROUD OWNER OF WHAT AMOUNTS TO A THIRTY-DOLLAR PLASTIC PITCHER.

CHECK-IN

Hi. My name is Snow White.

They call me Puffy.

I'm Prince Sparkle.

IN THE DEAD OF THE NIGHT, THE NEIGHBORHOOD PETS MET SECRETLY TO WORK THROUGH THE TRAUMA OF THEIR GIVEN NAMES.

HILARY Thanks to Kristin PRICE

THE ORIGINS of HEADACHES a time line in reverse

THE PLAY-GROUND

PARKING METER AILMENTS

THE EMPLOYEE FANTASY HOUR

"sigh"

BOSS, CAN I BOUNCE SOMETHING OFF YOU?

GO AHEAD.

HILARY B. PRICE

NEGOTIATIONS WITH *the* TOOTH FAIRY

USED TO BE I'D PUT A TOOTH UNDER MY PILLOW AND HOPE FOR A QUARTER...

NOW I PUT A QUARTER UNDER MY PILLOW AND HOPE FOR A TOOTH.

HILARY "Thanks to Kim" PRICE

HIGHWAY MODELS

CLOVERLEAF

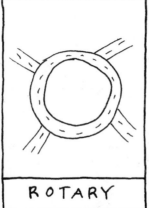

ROTARY

OVERPASS

MÖBIUS STRIP

HILARY B. PRICE

PAUL NEWMAN: a cross-generational perspective

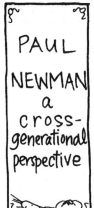

A DREAMBOAT OF EPIC PROPORTIONS!

AN INCREDIBLY HANDSOME OLDER MAN.

THAT <u>SALAD DRESSING</u> GUY?

HILARY B. PRICE

THE MONSTER-under-the-BED SUPPORT GROUP

THE IRONY IS, AFTER <u>YEARS</u> OF FAITHFUL SERVICE, I WAS REPLACED BY A HALF-DOZEN PLAYBOY MAGAZINES.

HILARY B. PRICE

BAKING BROWNIES: a guide to the human mind

1. READ BOX.
2. PREHEAT OVEN.
3. EMPTY MIX FROM BOX.
4. THROW BOX AWAY.
5. COMBINE INGREDIENTS.
6. FORGET INSTRUCTIONS.
7. FISH BOX FROM TRASH.

8. PUT MIX IN OVEN.
9. THROW BOX AWAY.
10. FORGET BAKING TIME.
11. FISH BOX FROM TRASH.
12. THROW.
13. FORGET.
14. FISH.

HILARY B. PRICE

THE ACUPUNCTURIST'S OFFICE

BY CONTRAST, DR. MINK FOUND THE APPOINTMENT REMINDER CARDS **SO** UNRELIABLE.

HILARY B. PRICE

THE CHANGING FACE of ROMANTIC LITERATURE

Chapter One

Sunset, after a fabulous meal. We sit out on the front porch, stuffed and happy. My love leans down to pass me a piece of nicotine gum, and we chew in silence as the liquid orange ball disappears behind the horizon.

HILARY B. PRICE

THE SHOPPING TRIP

CORN? NO, IT'S OUT OF SEASON.

PEACHES? THEY'RE OUT OF SEASON, TOO.

SORRY, RASPBERRIES, TOO.

WHAT? NO. CHEERIOS ARE NEVER OUT OF SEASON.

HILARY B. PRICE

SECRETS to SUCCESS: a guide for women

GET THIS—THEY SAY WOMEN ARE THREE TIMES AS LIKELY TO GET INTO A PROFESSIONAL ORCHESTRA IF THEY AUDITION BEHIND A SCREEN.

ARE YOU SURPRISED?

BOSS, I'M IN CUBICLE 64A, SECOND FLOOR... I'D LIKE A RAISE.

HILARY B. PRICE

THE EVIL EMPIRE

One vodka, please.

WHY IS IT EVERY SHOW OR MOVIE I SEE WE'RE FIGHTING SOME SLIMY ALIEN? WHATEVER HAPPENED TO A MORTAL ENEMY BEING A MERE MORTAL?!

I BLAME THE RUSSIANS.

PARDON?

THEY WERE OUR FAVORITE ENEMY! NOW THAT WE'RE ALLIES, WE HAVE TO FIGHT SOME UGLY ALIEN TO SECURE THE PLANET!

Tickets

YOU SOUND BITTER.

PEACE WON AT THE PRICE OF ENTERTAINMENT?? OF COURSE I'M BITTER.

HILARY B. PRICE

THE MYSTERIES of the WORLD EXPLAINED

WHY IS IT, WHENEVER A WHOLE FAMILY GETS INTO A CAR, THE DAD ALWAYS DRIVES?

THEY NEED SOMETHING TO DO WITH THEIR HANDS WHEN YOU TAKE AWAY THE REMOTE CONTROL.

BY HILARY. Thanks to KT. PRICE

A TRUE STORY

HAIR YOU GO!

SEEMS LIKE WHEREVER YOU GO, HAIR-CUTTING PLACES HAVE THE CORNIEST NAMES.

SHEAR BLISS!

WHAT ABOUT SOMETHING FOR THOSE OF US WHO ARE MORE SOPHISTICATED--

CURL UP & DYE

NEVER MIND.

DOLLY (THE LAMB CLONE) in NEW YORK CITY

I AM MY MOTHER'S SISTER. MY FATHER IS ALSO MY GRAND-FATHER...

I THINK I'M OEDIPUS REX WHEN I'M OFF MY MEDICATION. PERHAPS WE KNOW PEOPLE IN COMMON.

POST-BIRTHDAY PARTY

Dear Rex, Thanks for the stick. It was a perfect gift. xox Patches

Dear Stubbs, Great seeing you at my party. Loved the stick!! xox Patches

Dear Ginger, What a special day! The stick was so thoughtful. xox Patches

LIKE MOST, PATCHES LOATHED THE TEDIUM OF THANK-YOU NOTES.

HILARY "Thanks to P. Fimrite" PRICE

121

THE ENTREPRENEURS of TOMORROW

EVER NOTICE HOW ALL THE HIGH-CLASS SOAPS HAVE EXTREMELY BRITISH NAMES?

NOPE.

CRABTREE & EVELYN... CASWELL & MASSEY... YARDLEY OF LONDON... WHY SHOULD ENGLAND CORNER THE MARKET ON CLEANLINESS?!

WE SHOULD MARKET OUR OWN SOAP.

GOMEZ & EPSTEIN... IT HAS A NICE RING.

HILARY B. PRICE

THE MOM & POP STORES of TOMORROW

STEPMOM & POP

MOM & LIVE-IN BOYFRIEND

SALE

POP & POP

2 litre Soap 99¢

HILARY B. PRICE

THERAPY in the COMPUTER AGE

WHICH OF THESE BEST DESCRIBES HOW YOU FEEL?

:-(:-)   :-<

HILARY B. PRICE

So You're FINALLY MEETING the PARENTS

WHAT IT LOOKS LIKE...

WHAT IT FEELS LIKE...

HILARY B. PRICE

The HOME-COMING

Scope

click
ROWR!
ROWR!
ROWR!
ROWR!

HILARY B. PRICE

slurp
slurp
slurp
slurp
slurp
slurp
KLUNK!

NOTHING COMPLETES THE DAY LIKE A BIG DOG KISS.

THANK GOODNESS YOU'RE HERE. I HAD A TERRIBLE TASTE IN MY MOUTH.

The SECRET Rules to AMERICA'S Thriving CONSUMER ECONOMY

SKIPPING   LOITERING   HOPPING ON ONE FOOT

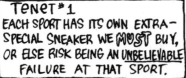

TeneT #1
EACH SPORT HAS ITS OWN EXTRA-SPECIAL SNEAKER WE MUST BUY, OR ELSE RISK BEING AN UNBELIEVABLE FAILURE AT THAT SPORT.

WELCOME TO FORGOTTENLAND!

TeneT #2
A BROKEN WATCHBAND MEANS A BROKEN WATCH, AND INVARIABLY CALLS FOR THE PURCHASE OF AN ENTIRELY NEW WATCH.

DEB'S FIX-O-RAMA
microwaves! LAMPS! TVs! VCRs! stereos! clocks! relation-ships!
SORRY-NO PHONE MACHINES or WATCHBANDS.

HILARY B. PRICE

TeneT #3
IT IS BAD & WRONG TO TEACH ANYONE TO REPAIR TELEPHONE ANSWERING MACHINES. THEY MUST REMAIN AS DISPOSABLE AS DIXIE CUPS.

THE INCIDENT

Matter of fact, I don't care for the curtains either.

TRAGICALLY, IT WASN'T UNTIL AFTER THE DECLAWING THAT FLUFFY'S OWNERS REALIZED IT WAS THE COUCH ITSELF SHE OBJECTED TO.

GASOLINE

MATCHES

YELLOW PAGES

A DAY IN THE LIFE

HILARY B. PRICE

THE SUMMIT

ALL IN FAVOR, PLEASE ROLL DOWN ON YOUR BACK AND SHOW ME YOUR SOFT UNDERBELLY.

HILARY B. PRICE

ACCLIMATING YOURSELF to the VEGETABLE WORLD: a beginners guide

START WITH BEGINNER VEGETABLES: CORN, PEAS & CARROTS. THEY CAN BE HIDDEN IN SOUP SO YOU'LL HARDLY KNOW THEY'RE THERE. START SLOWLY — DON'T PUSH IT.

ONCE YOU'VE BUILT UP YOUR STAMINA, MOVE ONTO THE INTERMEDIATE VEGETABLES: GREEN PEPPERS, BROCCOLI & ZUCCHINI. TRY THEM FIRST IN TV DINNERS SO THEY'RE JUST FLACCID GREEN BITS.

IF AND ONLY IF YOU'RE READY, MOVE ONTO THE ADVANCED VEGETABLES: BRUSSEL SPROUTS, KALE & BEETS. PROCEED WITH CAUTION. BRING A FRIEND FOR SUPPORT. MAKE SURE YOU'VE GOT A BIG GLASS OF MILK TO HELP WASH THEM DOWN.

NEW MALL STORES

PEACE & QUIET

NO MERCHANDISE — JUST SILENCE AND COMFORTABLE CHAIRS. PATRONS PAY BY THE HALF-HOUR.

HILARY B. PRICE

SUNLIGHT & FRESH AIR

CUSTOMERS CAN SPOIL THEMSELVES WITH IMPORTED AIR FROM THE RAIN FOREST AND SUNLIGHT FRESH FROM THE HAWAIIAN ISLANDS.

Small-Town Charm

FOR A ONE-TIME FEE, SHOPPERS CAN MUNCH PENNY CANDY WHILE PETTING THE OLD YELLOW DOG ON THE FRONT STOOP OF AN AUTHENTIC GENERAL STORE.

FIRST CONTACT

THE MILITIAMEN meet THE MINUTIAMEN

NO TAXES!! NO GOVERNMENT!! NO COMPROMISE!!!

YOUR FLANNEL SHIRT—IT'S PILLING.

HILARY B. PRICE

A MATTER of INTERPRETATION

TO SOME, PET-SITTING WAS A RESPONSIBILITY...

TO OTHERS, IT WAS A FORBIDDEN SPORT.

(NOTE: NO ANIMALS WERE HARMED IN THE MAKING OF THIS CARTOON.)

HILARY B. PRICE

RHYMES with ORANGE

1040 EZ TAX FORM	
1. How much do you make?	$.
2. Send it to us.	
U.S. Gov't Form 8675309 TOTAL	$.

HILARY B. PRICE